JOSTEDALSBREEN
NORWAY'S LARGEST GLACIER

View from Kjenndalskruna and the Lovatn lake. In the center, Ramnefjell and the rock slides that have filled portions of the lake. Photo: Finn Loftesnes

JOSTEDALS-BREEN

NORWAY'S LARGEST GLACIER

BJØRN WOLD OG
LEIF RYVARDEN

Translated by Donna Lunney Vear
and Brit Henschien

BOKSENTERET FORLAG

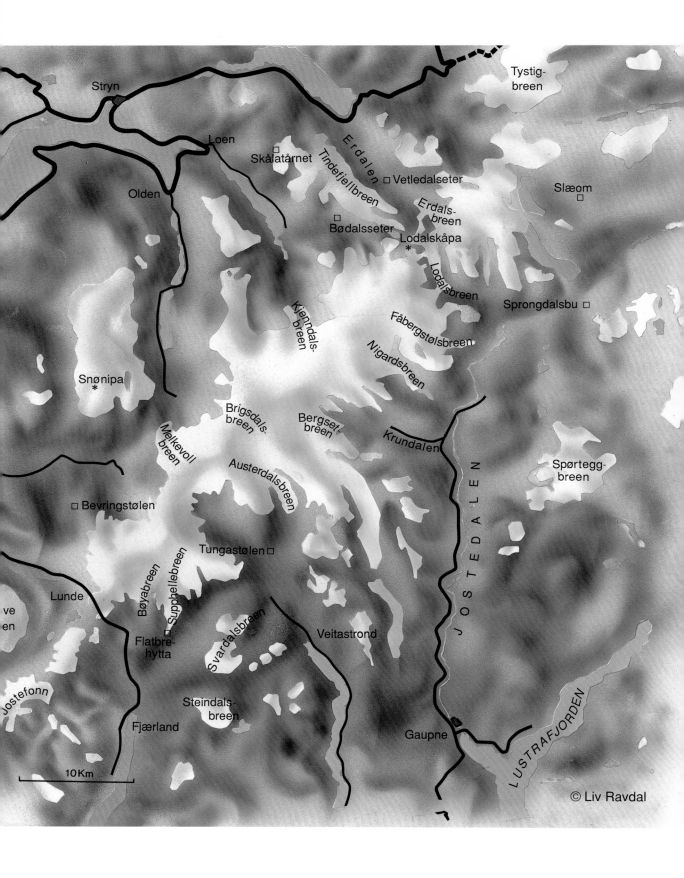

© Liv Ravdal

Contents

INTRODUCTION

Jostedalsbreen is the largest glacier on the European mainland. The enormous ice field covers a large part of the mountain area between Sogn and Nordfjord, an area of 487 square kilometers. In some places the glacier is more than 500 meters thick and has numerous branches that reach down into the surrounding valleys.

The valleys surrounding the Jostedalsbreen glacier are formed primarily by glacial activity. Therefore, they have a distinct U-shape such as the one shown here, the valley of Horpedalen in Fjærland. Photo: Bjørn Wold

Approaching the Bergsetbreen glacier in Jostedal, with the Baklibreen glacier at the right. The ice and the lush vegetation provide a strong contrast. Some glaciers reach far down to the forests, while others hide in higher side valleys. The valley of Krundalen in Jostedal is shown here. Photo: Bjørn Wold

Twenty-eight of these branches have names. The glacier plateau itself undulates evenly while the surrounding landscape is dramatic with precipitous mountains dropping down to the valleys. There are in fact only a few places where the glacier plateau is easily accessible.

The glacier is 80 kilometers long, while its width varies greatly. At its highest point it is more than 2000 meters above sea level and less than 100 meters above sea level at its lowest lying branch. Although snow and ice characterize the greater part of the national park, the surrounding valleys are lush and fertile.

The landscape of the glacier plateau is wavy with heights varying from around 1750 meters to around 1950 meters. The highest point is Høgste Breakulen at 1957 meters above sea level. Because this peak is made of ice, its height can vary from year to year. Nearby, a nunatak, a mountain completely surrounded by glacier ice, can be seen. The cairn atop it is a few meters lower than the highest point of the glacier. However, the highest mountaintop in the area is Lodalskåpa, 2083 meters above sea level, a distinct peak on the northern side of the glacier.

Approaching the glacial ice cap with a view toward the Tuftebreen glacier in Jostedal. Photo: Bjørn Wold

The valleys around the glacier are typical U-valleys with steep sides and flat floors. These valleys have been formed as the glacier moved down the mountain over a period of several ice ages spanning millions of years.

Hanging valleys and cirques along the mountainsides indicate that the glacier has been much larger and more extensive. Today, branches of the glacier protrude high up on the mountainside, others extend all the way down to the valley floor, at an altitude of 300 – 400 meters above sea level. Several of the glacier branches are currently advancing and are literally pushing their way into the forest. The lowest is the Kjenndalsbreen glacier in Loen, which now reaches all the way down to a birch forest at about 160 meters above sea level. In Fjærland, only 60 meters above sea level, lies the Supphellebreen glacier. This is a so-called 'regenerated' glacier. It is not connected to the main glacier, but is sustained by avalanches from it.

Wild and forceful streams and rivers cascade down the mountainsides giving life to the landscape. Large outwash plains and deltas can be found where the river has left behind much of the gravel and sand it has carried from the glacier. Even farther

The lush Loen and Lovatn lakes.
Photo: Finn Loftesnes

Paddling a canoe along the Austdalsbreen glacier can be fascinating, but use extreme caution. The icebergs can tip over without warning and create powerful waves.
Photo: Finn Loftesnes

View from Kjenndalskruna over the Krunebreen glacier and Lovatn lake. Vestiges of the ancient mountain plateau are a distinct landmark on the horizon.
Photo: Bjørn Wold

down lie several ponds and lakes with their characteristic green color. They fill basins formed by earlier glaciers, often with a terminal moraine as a dam.

Geology

The bedrock in the national park consists primarily of gneiss, a rather hard species of rock which has few minerals. Despite this, vegetation is abundant and varied, due to large amounts of fine mud and clay deposited by the glacier rivers. As this is virgin soil containing many minerals in a readily available form, it provides a good foundation for plant growth. It also holds water easily, which is important for vegetation.

The gneiss and other rock types under and around the glacier were formed during prehistoric times, which means they are between 1000 and 1800 million years old.

The plateau where the glacier lies today was born approximately 450 million years ago. At that time a large mountain chain was pushed up by powerful movements of the earth's surface. The erosive forces began their work immediately, with the help of water, frost and ice.

Smoothed and rounded mountains in front of the Nigardsbreen glacier.
Photo: Nils Haakensen

After a time the entire mountain chain was ground down to form a smooth flat plain. About 50 million years ago the plain rose about 2000 meters, and the plateau where the Jostedalsbreen glacier lies today was formed. Remnants of this highland plain can still be found many places around the Jostedalsbreen National Park, but the deep valleys and narrow fjords make it difficult to see the contours of this ancient flat landscape.

Weather and climate

Jostedalsbreen National Park is situated between 61 and 62 degrees north latitude. This latitude is normally associated with an arctic climate, as in Greenland, for example, which is at the same latitude. Even though weather conditions on top of the glacier can be fairly harsh, the climate cannot be called arctic, due to the strong influence of mild and humid winds from the sea.

In midwinter many of the people in the communities around the glacier are not able to see the sun except as a reflection on the mountain peaks. On the other hand, if one stands on the glacier the sun will be above the horizon for five or six hours. At midsummer, it is visible for 19 hours from the glacier. But an almanac is one thing and reality is another, particularly on the Jostedalsbreen glacier. That the humid air becomes more dense forming clouds and fog is not an unknown phenomenon for those who have spent

Jostedalen and the glacier in winter light.
Photo: Finn Loftesnes

a lot of time on mountains or glaciers. The most stable periods of good weather, with scarce cloud cover, usually come in April and May.

Bad weather coming in from the sea can have a strong impact on top of the glacier. This is most pronounced in the fall and winter. The weather conditions on the glacier will generally be even worse than along the coast. Some years may bring gale force winds and storms almost every day during the winter. As spring progresses, the intensity of the weather conditions diminishes, the winds become more gentle and less frequent. But even in the summer one can expect to encounter occasional strong winds, although the average winds can be described as 'moderate breezes'.

Precipitation comes primarily with warm, damp air from the southwest and west. When the air is pushed up against the mountains, it becomes cold and is cooled even more as it moves further over the glacier. Consequently, it loses its ability to hold moisture, and occasionally causes large amounts of precipitation over a short period of time. Although it can rain at the top of the glacier even in midwinter, the greatest amount of precipitation falls as snow in the period from September to June. Most of the snowfall occurs from

October to the end of February. These are large quantities of snow, and up on the glacier plateau it is not unusual to find six to eight meters of snow during winter, and ten meters have been recorded during years with large amounts of precipitation. These measurements reflect the depth of the snow over a large area, and not just at snowdrifts.

One would perhaps think that air temperatures would be very low on the glacier. However, this is not the case even though it can of course be cold, and is generally colder than in the surrounding communities. The lowest temperatures are carried by cold air from the north, or they occur on clear, calm nights. In midwinter, temperatures on the Jostedalsbreen glacier are normally between minus 10 and minus 20 degrees Celsius. It is not unusual for temperatures to rise dramatically in connection with extremely bad weather, and temperatures can rise above freezing and be accompanied by rain

The fog can be incredibly thick. Here, one can catch a glimpse of the cabins at Steinmannen, but out on the white surface of the glacier nothing can be seen in these conditions. Photo: Bjørn Wold

On the glacier during a snow storm. Photo: Tom Dybwad

several times during a winter season. Evidence of this can be observed as thick layers of ice in the snow later in the year.

As spring progresses the average temperature rises quickly, and in May it reaches minus three to minus four degrees Celsius. During the summer months the average temperature is around plus four degrees Celsius. Even then temperatures can vary greatly, and it is not unusual to have temperatures below zero and snow even in midsummer. Because of the intense radiation and reflection from the surface of the snow it can seem very warm when the wind is still, even

Spending the night on the glacial plateau. In favorable conditions, camping spots are usually plentiful.
Photo: Per Goller

though the air temperature rarely rises above approximately plus 10 degrees Celsius.

Exact weather data is scarce because until recently there have not been permanent meteorological stations in year-round operation on the Jostedalsbreen glacier. The Norwegian Water Resources and Energy Administration (NVE) has operated summer stations for several years, for example at Steinmannen on the Nigardsbreen glacier (1633 meters above sea level). This station is now in continuous operation. The Norwegian Glacier Museum operates a year-round station at the Flatbreen glacier in Fjærland. The station even has a telephone answering machine with a weather report. You can try it yourself by dialing 57 69 32 89. In addition, the Norwegian Geotechnical Institute operates a weather station in the Breiddalen valley, at approximately 1700 meters above sea level. Data can be obtained any time of the day at the Jostedalsbreen National Park Centre.

THE GLACIER BECKONS

A glacier hike can be many things, and there are probably many who have had ambivalent feelings toward the glacier on their first trip. On the one hand one may feel excited and appreciate the beauty of it, on the other, it is frightening, unfamiliar and dangerous. Most people first become acquainted with a glacier with the help of a guide. Today it is easy to find both a guide and hiking possibilities on the glacier, even for those who do not themselves have the know-how and equipment.

The Nigardsbreen glacier has long been a major hiking glacier for motoring tourists because it is easy to reach, and because the people in Jostedalen realized early on the potential in conducting guided tours for tourists. From its start as a modest business in the 1970's, Jostedal Breførerlag, which now runs the guide service, has grown so enormously that it has almost become a year-round business. On the Nigardsbreen glacier you can rent all the necessary equipment and obtain a guide for all types of hikes and ski trips, from a short

A group of tourists on a rope walking down the ice fall after circling the Nigardsbreen. Photo: Pål Hermansen

one-hour family trip at the mouth of the glacier to a several day trip up ice falls and over the large glacier. There are major activities here every day, regardless of the weather, all summer long.

There are also guides available in other places around the Jostedalsbreen glacier: in Jostedal, Jølster, Olden, Bødalen, Oppstryn and Fjærland. During the summer season a number of day and week tours are offered.

Hiking the blue ice

What one most often associates with a glacier is cold, blue ice, crevasses, towers, ice ridges and icy water. We get crampons for our boots and are tied to guide ropes. The guide gives his instructions. The first hesitant steps onto the ice confirm our apprehensions. It is slippery, but thanks to the crampons and the trail the guide has cut, it goes surprisingly well. The ice can be sharp and those without gloves or mittens soon have small cuts on their hands. Furthermore, the ice is not as clean as many believe. Quite the contrary, we become dirty rather quickly if we are not careful. But we should be careful anyway. Falling on blue ice is not fun. One gets both wet and dirty, and can easily get cut in places where skin is exposed. Consequently, people are usually asked to wear sufficient clothing. This is wise for another reason. At the mouth

You can decide how difficult your climb on the blue ice will be, according to ability and preference.
Photo: Anne Kjos-Wenjum

of the glacier it is often windy, particularly on nice days. This is called a 'glacier wind.' The air over the glacier has been chilled and is heavier than the air surrounding it. Because it thus sinks, you will almost always encounter a headwind on the way up a glacier. A glacier wind is strongest on nice days, and particularly in the afternoon when the sun has warmed up the mountain surfaces adjacent to the glacier.

A trip on the blue ice is fascinating and exciting, despite the discomforts, or perhaps because of them. It opens up a totally new world: the colors, the diversity, the constantly being careful not to fall, the excitement at seeing a glacier crevasse, the awe-inspiring deep fissures in the ice, and water that runs in many directions and the many different ice formations. Oh, yes, a trip on the blue ice can provide lifelong memories.

Glacier courses

If your first meeting with a glacier fascinates you so much that you want to learn more and perhaps be able to manage on your own, the simplest way to go about this is to sign up for a glacier course. Such a course teaches you what a glacier is, what dangers await you and how they can be avoided so that you can move around safely. It is important that training includes a combination of theory and practice. Training should not only take place in the areas of blue ice. The most important part of the training should take place in the transition areas where the blue ice and the snow covered areas meet. These areas are the most dangerous and difficult to master.

After World War II there was little interest in hiking on glaciers, but the non-profit organization, The Norwegian Mountain Touring Association (DNT), arranged a course for guides at Bødalsseter in 1948. Ten years after this course, DNT began to train guides again, this time for the glaciers in Jotunheimen. These courses were the precursors of the glacier courses that were organized in Finse around 1960. In order to stimulate interest in glacier hiking among people from nearby communities, courses were eventually started other places. In the mid-1960's, DNT also started courses at Flatbrehytta in Fjærland in cooperation with the well-known and certified guide, Anders Øygaard. People from the communities around the glacier were originally given priority to participate in the Flatbre courses, but as there was little interest the courses were filled with people from other parts of the country. Nevertheless, this planted the first seeds of interest in

A course in glacier hiking on the Bødalsbreen glacier. Photo: Anne Kjos-Wenjum

*Above: Rescue techniques are an important part of the glacier course. With sufficient technical knowledge and equipment, a person who has fallen into a crevasse can climb back up alone.
Photo: Leif Ryvarden*

*Above left: A mystical atmosphere in the ice; looking upward from the bottom of a crevasse.
Photo: Finn Loftesnes*

Hiking on blue ice. With a glacier course, and simple equipment, you can have many exciting trips on your own. Photo: Finn Loftesnes

17

the local communities. Later, courses were arranged at Bødalsseter and Fåbergstølen in Jostedal. In Jostedalen, the Jostedal Breførarlag (a guide association) arranges annual glacier courses and various other types of courses are now held many places around the Jostedalsbreen glacier.

Ice climbing

If excitement and challenges are what one is looking for, ice climbing can be an interesting alternative to glacier hiking, and to mountain climbing, for that matter. Today, ice climbing often takes place on frozen waterfalls in the winter, but one can also find the same excitement and challenges on a glacier. There, precipitous glacier falls with enormous crevasses, and huge ice walls and towers offer a variety of challenges. These challenges are not just of a technical nature. It is more important to evaluate potential risks, not least, the possibility of an avalanche. It is important to remember that the glacier is

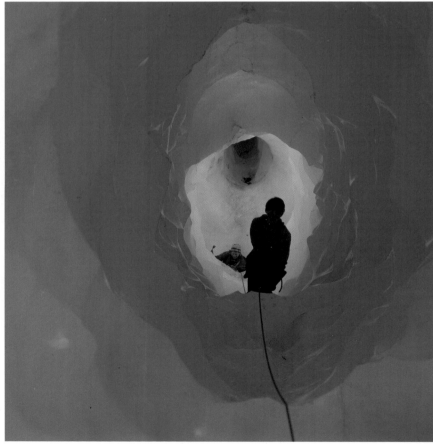

in constant motion and that an avalanche can occur at any time, if conditions are right.

Exploring with Slingsby

For most of us a trip on the Jostedalsbreen glacier will mean crossing the large snow covered plateau. In the summer of 1881, the famous English mountaineer, William Cecil Slingsby, crossed the Jostedalsbreen glacier together with the Norwegian mountain guide, Johannes Vigdal. They started from Tverrdalssetra in the Tunsbergdalen valley at four o'clock in the morning. They climbed up almost all of the Tunsbergdalsbreen glacier, Norway's longest glacier arm, before they turned north to Høgste Breakulen. After six hours of 'hard toil' they reached the top. Slingsby was clearly disappointed with what he saw, which he described as "about the most topless mountain I had ever been on." He was used to large expanses of snow, but not prepared for a 'white Sahara.' Nevertheless, he said in his report: "It was in some respects a most impressive view, and I am glad to have seen it. Where else on the Jostedalsbre can you get the same idea of enormous space."

Slingsby and Vigdal continued their trip westward and, as Slingsby wrote, "All at once a snowy bay opened out before us,

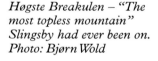

To the right: William Cecil Slingsby.

Høgste Breakulen – "The most topless mountain" Slingsby had ever been on. Photo: Bjørn Wold

with a view of séracs and rocks far down below." Initially, they did not know which valley lie before them. After a while they realized it was the Kjenndalsbreen glacier, and after a dramatic descent they finally arrived at the community of Nesdal at nine thirty that evening.

*The Tunsbergdalsbreen glacier – in early summer while still covered with snow from the winter.
Photo: Bjørn Wold*

*An ice fall on the Kjenndalsbreen glacier, which Slingsby and Vigdal descended. Ice avalanches are frequent here.
Photo: Bjørn Wold*

On your own

The first people to venture forth over the glacier felt the thrill of discovery, but also the uncertainty of approaching unknown terrain. Even today it is possible to feel the joy of discovery with each new trip, but most prefer having some information about the trip they are planning to embark upon. For many the planning is just as exciting and rewarding as the trip itself. For some the planning itself is enough.

Increased interest in the glacier has led to the need for more detailed descriptions of the routes, including those less frequently traveled. Consequently, the Norwegian Mountain Touring Association (DNT) published the first issue of *Breføreren – rutebeskrivelser for breturer i Norge*, a handbook of glacier routes in Norway. This publication provides a comprehensive description of the Jostedalsbreen National Park and surrounding areas. Almost a hundred different routes are described.

Beneath Kattenakken, looking toward the Brigsdalsbreen glacier – which is now expanding and threatening the lake.
Photo: Anne Kjos-Wenjum

On the way home from Lodalskåpa.
Photo: Finn Loftesnes

Hiking

Some of the greatest experiences of outdoor life in Norway can be found on a hike over the Jostedalsbreen glacier. It is physically demanding, but will undoubtedly also be a great adventure. The ascent to the glacier is sure to be warm and wet – either from rain or perspiration. It is a steep climb, occasionally very steep, but oh the satisfaction you feel when you finally manage to reach the top.

On a clear day, from the top of the glacier, you can follow the path of the sun all day, including those few hours when it is below the horizon. In early summer, such nights on the glacier offer nuances of light otherwise found only in arctic regions. Down in the narrow valleys around the glacier the sun disappears early in the evening.

It is not easy to predict the weather for the innermost areas of Sogn og Fjordane. Therefore it is quite likely you will encounter weather that is quite different from that which has been predicted. There can be large differences between the weather in the valleys around the glacier and that on the glacier. The glacier is often a weather divide between Nordfjord and Sogn. A northerly wind can, for example, bring really nice weather to Jostedalen and Fjærland. At the same time it can be overcast in Nordfjord, and there can be heavy fog on the glacier. A southerly wind creates the opposite effect. Thus, a great deal of experience is necessary to interpret weather forecasts correctly. This is especially true in the summer months when the winds are calmer. On the other hand, extremes of really good or bad weather will be the same over the entire area.

Some places require a bit of climbing. On these occasions, it is best not to be afraid of heights. Be careful in bad weather!
Photo: Bjørn Wold

Splendor and danger

You can experience a sense of splendor many places on the snow-covered ice field. There are a number of relatively easy trails

Sunset over Supphellenipa. New snow can fall on the glacier even in the summer months.
Photo: Finn Loftesnes

crossing the glacier. The difficult part is going up from, or down to, the valleys on either side of the glacier. Today it is not customary to climb the ice falls, even though there are a large number of both marked and unmarked trails up the mountainside and onto the mountain ridges on both sides of the glacier. If you follow these trails, the edge of the glacier will almost always look like an innocent patch of snow. Do not be fooled. This is precisely what is most treacherous about glaciers, that one cannot see where danger lurks. The crevasses are indeed there, hidden under the snow. All glaciers have crevasses, but they are often covered by varying thicknesses of snow. Because of this, you should always use a rope and know enough about glaciers to avoid the most dangerous areas when you set out on a hike. When you have enough experience and know the area well, you will be able to cross some areas without a rope, at least on skis. But crossing without a rope is the exception rather than the rule!

Various crossings

Ice falls offer many challenges, and man becomes insignificant in relation to nature. Photo: Bjørn Wold

If we start in the south, there is a popular and relatively easy crossing from Fjærland to Jølster, with two destinations: one at Lunde,

deep in Kjøsnesfjorden, and one in the Stardalen valley. The relatively short trips from Flatbrehytta over to Veitastrond are also popular, but these trips do not bring you onto the main glacier.

One of the very best, but toughest and most difficult trips, is from Tungastølen in Veitastrond via the Austerdalsbreen glacier, Kvitesteinsvarden and Kattenakken down to Brigsdal deep in the Oldedalen valley. If you start early you can catch the morning sun at the Austerdalsbreen glacier. This glacier, which Slingsby described as "the finest ice scenery in Europe," is quite special with its crawfish tail pattern and the three dramatic ice falls named after the three Nordic gods, Loki, Odin and Thor, at the farthest reaches of the glacier. The route crosses over some large lateral moraines and on to the relatively flat 'crawfish tail glacier' which is relatively free of crevasses and easy to hike. The trail goes to Odin's falls, the middle of the three ice falls. After climbing some distance up Odin's falls, the trail continues into the mountain area on the left. This can be a very difficult section of the trip, and during summers with little snow on the ground, it can be almost impossible to reach the top. Because of this, the trip should not be undertaken from the opposite direction before one is sure the route is passable. The trail continues further to Kvitesteinsvarden (about 1400 meters above sea level) and is steep and difficult. All along the trail you can hear the roar of

Even long rope teams seem small in this enormous landscape. Tverrfjell is on the right and Lodalskåpa is in the background. This was the route for cattle drives in the old days.
Photo: Anne Kjos-Wenjum

*In the summer, nights are
long and light. At the height
of summer, one can almost
follow the sun's journey
around the entire horizon.
Photo: Finn Loftesnes*

The view from Kvitesteins-varden toward the Auster-dalsbreen glacier shaped like a crawfish tail. The ice bands seen here have formed because the ice that passes through the ice falls is in the winter is cleaner and holds more snow than the summer ice. Photo: Finn Loftesnes

ice loosening from Thor's falls in the distance. As is usual when hiking the Jostedalsbreen glacier, the rewards are great when one finally reaches the top. The view, and the experience itself, are hard to describe, let alone photograph. They have to be experienced first hand.

From the Kvitesteinsvarden cairn the trail heads northwest. Here the trail is almost always covered with snow, and you must remember that there can be many hidden crevasses. When the view opens up to the west, it is vital that you identify the Slingsbyvarden cairn. It can be difficult to find, particularly in the fog, because it lies on a little reef of ice a bit down the glacier trough toward the Oldedalen valley. There are always a number of crevasses between Slingsby-varden and Kattenakken, so it can take time to find a good route. Kattenakken is a sharp ridge that rises up between the Melkevoll-breen and Kjøtabreen glaciers. You can get the best view of the Ol-dedalen valley and the Brigsdalsbreen glacier by crossing over the top of the ridge. It is exposed, but it is not difficult.

Further north there are a number of fine trails from Jostedal to Olden and Loen. All of them involve long trips on the glacier pla-teau, allowing you to appreciate the vastness of the glacier. But you will also realize that walking for hours in wet summer snow can be heavy going. Farthest north in Jostedalen we come to the popular passage between Fåbergstølen and the Erdalen valley in Oppstryn.

Major cairns

We have already mentioned Kvitesteinsvarden and Slingsbyvarden. These are just two of the most famous major cairns around the edge of the Jostedalsbreen glacier. These huge stone cairns were built years ago to show where the paths down to the communities began. Some of them look almost like a human being or a sign-post. The Steinmannen (the stone man) – marking the beginning of one of the paths down to Jostedalen – is a good example. It is very important to have a reliable starting point before you begin

Taking a well-earned rest at the Kvitesteinsvarden cairn above Austerdalsbreen. Photo: Finn Loftesnes

the trip down to the valley. If you do not find the right path, you could quickly find yourself on a steep rocky slope, or on the edge of a precipice or a cleft. If you do not find the landmark you are looking for, it might be safer and easier to go all the way back over the glacier again. It is precisely these difficult trails down to the valleys that make hiking on the glacier plateau so demanding. In good weather it is a delight and pleasure and everything seems relatively simple. But the weather can change quickly, and when it does it can be difficult, sometimes impossible, to find a safe path down from the glacier.

Rucksacks tend to bulge when packing for a long trip, but the national flag is a must on the 17th of May! Photo: Per Goller

Hiking the length of the glacier

One of Norway's major wilderness trails crosses the Jostedalsbreen glacier lengthwise, which means it follows the entire glacier ridge, and is usually crossed from north to south. Starting at Grotli or at Bråtå in Skjåk and ending up at the highway crossing Gaularfjellet, is the most challenging route. But there are many alternatives. In recent years, starting at Mysubuttsetra in Sjåk or at Greidung in Oppstryn has been very popular. A great place to end is at the Flatbrehytta cabin from which you continue down the steep, but manageable, trail to Fjærland.

This trip takes several days, and one of Norway's long holiday weekends in May is a good time to take the trip. At this time of year

The view from Lodalskåpa toward the northeast; Tverr-fjell on the left and Stornosi on the right.
Photo: Finn Lofesnes

the weather is stable and skiing conditions are good. This is actually a ski trip; to attempt it on foot is reckless.

Those who have made the trip in good weather with good skiing conditions, and are unaware of the dangers, may think this is a simple and safe trip. It is not! You should not choose this trip unless you have the right equipment and extensive knowledge of glaciers. There are, in particular, two ever-present dangers: glacier crevasses hidden under a thin cover of snow and the fact that it can be very difficult to ski down again should the weather turn bad.

One of the hardest parts of the trip is the climb up Småttene. These are steep ice falls that plunge down from the plateau between Brenibba and Lodalskåpa. They are not just steep, but also full of crevasses and are occasionally dangerous because of the threat of avalanches. You must use a rope and know what to do if someone falls into a crevasse.

After a difficult but exciting 800 meter climb, it is perhaps time to find a place to camp. Many choose Ståleskar. If you have any energy left, you can take an evening stroll on Lodalskåpa to get a good view of the rest of the trip south. When snow conditions are good, this is a straightforward trip, but you must be careful – and not be afraid of heights.

With an early start and good skiing conditions, you can quickly head south over the first hills and down into the basin between the Nigardsbreen and Krunebreen glaciers. To the right, Kjenndalskruna rises like a sharp ridge out of the glacier, and Høgste Breakulen can be seen off in the distance. While you are struggling along the seemingly endless hills, you can find comfort in the fact that you have just passed the area where the Jostedalsbreen glacier is thickest. Between 500 and 600 meters of glacier ice separate you from the mountain floor. Up here, with this fantastic view, you really feel as if you are on the top of Norway. If the weather is good, you can enjoy a long lunch on the southern slope below the cairn on Høgste. On the other hand, if the weather is about to turn bad, this is a good place to consider an alternative path down to civilization. A good ski trail runs down from the glacier, northeast toward Steinmannen and through Hauganosi. The ridge south of the Krundalen valley sloping down toward Tverranibba and the Røykjedalen valley is also a good choice. There are also a couple of easy descents which take you to Olden. If you continue south, however, you will have to get all the way down toward Fjærland and Jølster in order to find paths that you can ski down in the winter.

As you journey onward, the terrain from Høgste is more varied. Mountain reefs appear and you will struggle up yet another long hill to another large plateau. Having crossed this plateau, you will fly down in the direction of the narrowest point of the glacier, Bing's Hollow. This is a fairly large depression formed and reinforced by extreme winds every winter, and maintained by thaws and water during the summer. This can be an exotic camping site before the reasonably long trip awaiting you the next day. You have plenty of time to decide which route to take.

Most choose the trail that passes Supphellenipa and then continues down Flatbreen glacier to Flatbrehytta and Fjærland. But the trips down to the Bevringsdalen valley in Jølster or further south across Jostefonn to Gaularfjellet are also good. If you are familiar with mountaintouring and want more of a challenge, there are several other possibilities, but study the map carefully.

Preparing for the descent. When leaving the Flatbreen glacier, it is a steep downhill run to Fjærland. Photo: Bjørn Wold

Other long trips

If you find it too crowded along the center of the glacier, finding good alternatives that are just as marvelous and challenging is not a problem. An exciting mountain ridge runs between the Stardalen valley and Olden where Snønipa, the Myklebustbreen glacier and Sisliekruna are well worth a visit. Or why not try the ridges on both sides of the Tunsbergdalsbreen glacier? Here you will find many

challenges. The best ski trip in the entire area is perhaps the one along the ridge between the Lodalen valley and the Erdalen valley/Oppstryn. Strictly speaking, this is not part of the Jostedalsbreen glacier itself, but is still a part of the Jostedalsbreen National Park. If you are approaching from the north, the route goes up a steep incline north/northwest of Tverrfjellet. This is definitely a fairweather trip. It offers variety and fun, but you have to be in good shape and not afraid of heights. There is a lot of skiing uphill and downhill in this terrain, and much of it is very steep. Nevertheless, you will be rewarded many times over for your efforts, particularly when you take in the view straight down to Strynevatnet lake, 1900 meters below you. Another reward is arriving at what is perhaps the most unique tourist cabin in the country, Skålatårnet. Before you reach it you will have passed the Skålbreen glacier, Bings ice cap and Tindefjell, just to name a few of the highlights of the trip.

Skiing in Ståleskardet. Where is the best camping place? Photo: Tom Dybwad

Top: Evening atmosphere at a campsite. Photo: Bjørn Wold

Left: Rope is always necessary for the climb up the Småttene ice falls! Photo: Finn Loftesnes

HIKING NEAR JOSTEDALSBREEN

The approaches to the glacier are steep and often difficult to find. Take note of any landmark cairns and signs along the way.
Photo: Bjørn Wold

Even if you have never been on a glacier or taken a glacier course, there are a number of great hiking trails to choose from near the Jostedalsbreen glacier. These provide you with ample opportunity to experience the many and striking aspects of the glacier. DNT has several cabins enabling you to take longer hikes. In addition, the many shorter day trips can be rewarding, whether you wend your way back to a hotel or an inn or have come by car and are staying in a tent. All you need is good hiking equipment, and do not forget warm, water-repellent clothing! The weather changes quickly near the Jostedalsbreen glacier.

What follows is a description of hiking possibilities in the area around the glacier, starting in the north, and following the sun around the glacier to Strynefjellet on the west side.

Trips and activities on the glacier itself are described in a separate chapter.

Grotli – Hjelle

This is a great trip. On the first day you cross the mountains south of Grotli and end up at the self-service cabin called Skridulaupbui at the deepest point in the Rauddalen valley. You will have joined one of the old routes from Nordfjord to the upper Gudbrandsdalen valley. People and animals have been using this route up until 1894, when the road over Strynefjellet was completed.

The next day you travel westward through the narrow and beautiful pass between the Tystigbreen glacier on the north and the Sikilbreen glacier on the south. The path down Kamperhamrane runs partly down stone steps built around 1800. There are no longer overnight facilities at Sunndalsseter. From Sunndalsseter it is only a couple of hours down a good cart road to the Hjelledalen valley and civilization.

Returning to spring.
Photo: Finn Loftesnes

Slæom – over Sognskardet to Hjelle

If you are in good shape, you can take the same route back to the
Sunndalen valley, but instead of retracing the route to the Raudalen
valley, you can go through Sognskardet and up the steep incline
leading to the Sognskardsbreen glacier and then down to Kupvatnet
lake. Traversing the glacier is not complicated and the signs at the
entrance and exit are easy to spot. The trail on the glacier is no more
than about two kilometers, but if you do not have previous
experience you should use a guide.

This age-old passage connecting west and east is shorter than the Rauddal trail, and when you have reached Mysubuttdalen valley, it is very easy to go on from there. The self-service cabin, Slæom, located at the top of Mysubuttdalen valley is a nice place to spend the night. The next day you hike down to one of DNT's finest cabins, Sotaseter. From here you can choose one of many trails leading north and south.

The Fåbergstøl outwash plain is the largest in Norway. In our time, the consistent addition of material, primarily from the Stegholtbreen glacier, keeps them active.
Photo: Bjørn Wold

Sota – Styggevatn – Sprongdalshytta

From Sota there are two trails to upper Jostedalen. One goes through the Øvre Sprongdalen valley and is the easiest. If, however, you want to inspect the new dam at the Styggevatn lake, you can take the trail north of Sprongdalseggi, down to the lake and then over to the dam. This is the site of the old trail, and Styggevasshytta was previously situated where the rock debris from making the dam has been placed. In order to reach Sprongdalshytta you must either go over Sprongdalseggi or take the trail down to Sprongdøla and then up again to the cabin. Both routes are marked.

The Lodalsbreen glacier with the dark tower of Lodalskåpa in the background. The medial moraine is created where the ice masses from the Småttene falls on the left meet the ice from the Strupbreen glacier on the right, at the base of Lodalskåpa. Photo: Finn Loftesnes

Fåbergstølsgrandane

At Fåbergstølen, the highest point in the Jostedalen valley, lies Få-bergstølsgrandane, Norway's largest outwash plain. You should treat yourself to a trip into the Stordalen valley to the edge of the Lodals-breen glacier, where you will wander through the history of Norway's ice age and see how glaciers, rock slides, and glacier rivers have shaped our country. The trail into the Stordalen valley is unmarked, but the valley floor is easy to follow and it is full of experiences, whether they be the sight of beautiful flowers growing on sand banks, the steep mountains or the mighty glacier river, gray with glacier sludge, cutting a path through the earth. Large sand banks are constantly being formed, while others are washed away within a few hours. A book title *A Restlessness that Never Dies...* by the Norwegian author, Fredrik Wandrup, best describes this phenomenon.

River water in the Nigards-dalen valley, with the Nigardsbreen glacier in the background.
Photo: Finn Loftesnes

Rivers emerging from glaciers are fascinating, but it is extremely dangerous to go near them, or into them. No one can predict the sudden fall of blocks of ice. The river can be blocked beneath this ice, and when this kind of dam gives way, tremendous amounts of ice and water pour forth without warning.
Photo: Bjørn Wold

Hiking on the Nigardsbreen glacier.
Photo: Finn Loftesnes

In the summer of 1986, 250,000 tons of ice from the Baklibreen glacier fell 700 meters into the valley of Krundalen.
Photo: Bjørn Wold

38

Nigardsbreen

The Nigardsbreen glacier, on the west side of Jostedalen, is perhaps Norway's most famous glacier branch. Like a snake, it winds down a narrow valley from the glacier plateau and ends on dry land above the western shore of the Nigardsvatnet lake. When you turn off the main road and head toward the lake, recall that in 1750 the glacier was about 40 meters high here, illustrating how quickly a glacier expands and contracts in size. The Nigardsvatnet lake appeared in 1930, so the glacier has receded significantly in just the last 50 years.

The easiest way to reach the ice front is by boat over the lake, but you can also reach it by taking a half-hour hike along the north side of the lake. At the glacier's edge you must obey the strict rules that apply when you are this close to the glacier. The glacier can suddenly crack and calve, and the roar of the river can drown out all other sounds.

The river flowing from out of the entrance to the glacier carries with it large amounts of sediments, about 20,000 tons in an average year. Half of this is deposited on the delta, and some of it is deposited in the lake where it sinks to the bottom. Lesser amounts

The Veitastrondsvatnet lake and the community in the background make a deep impression in the massive mountain range that borders the glacier.
Photo: Finn Loftesnes

Austerdalsbreen: "The finest ice scenery in Europe." The ice falls are named after Nordic gods, Thor on the right, Odin in the middle and Loki on the left. The route from Tungastølen to Brigsdal runs up the mountain between Odin and Loke's ice falls. The gravel running down the middle of the glacier is a medial moraine, created and deposited by erosion on either side of the mountain peak.
Photo: Finn Loftesnes

are carried to the other end of the lake and down the Jostedøla river.

The area around the Nigardsbreen glacier has been declared a national reserve.

Bergsetbreen

Many consider the Bergsetbreen glacier, located deep inside the Krundalen valley, the Jostedalsbreen glacier's most spectacular outlet glacier. Leave the road at Gjerde in Jostedalen and park at the Bergset farm a few kilometers into the valley. From here it takes about an hour on a good trail along the floor of the valley to reach the falls. The Bergsetbreen glacier is a fantastic sight in that it appears to consist of a single hanging wall of ice, and you will marvel at the fact that the ice does not come crashing down into the valley at the slightest movement. You will not find a steeper or higher glacier falls anywhere in Norway. Photo opportunities abound where the lushness of the valley floor stands in sharp contrast to the icy wall, with the edge of the glacier sparkling under a bright blue sky.

Here, as always, do not approach the ice falls even though the glacier appears calm and stable. A Dutch family was killed here, the victims of a powerful ice avalanche originating at the Baklibreen glacier on the northwest side of the valley. Follow instructions!

Austerdalsbreen

The long Veitastrondvatnet lake lies like a shiny serpent between precipitous mountainsides. It is easy to understand that Veitasrondsbygda, at the end of the lake, was isolated for long periods in the winter because of numerous avalanches near the lake. Only when the lake froze did the inhabitants of this community have a safe route to Hafslo and civilization. Today the road has many tunnels, providing year-round connections.

The road ends at Tungastølen, a good starting point for a hike to the Austerdalsbreen glacier's wonderful ice cap. After a little over an

A campsite on Supphelleryggen with a view over the Flatbreen glacier and Fjærlandsfjorden.
Photo: Finn Loftesnes

Flatbrehytta is a popular self-service cabin at the edge of the Flatbreen glacier in Fjærland, shown here on a beautiful day!
Photo: Bjørn Wold

hour into the valley on good trails, you arrive at the tongue of the glacier which stretches about two kilometers in an almost horizontal direction into the valley. The glacier is firm and easy to walk on, with no crevasses. It divides into three beautiful glacier falls: Torsbreen, Lokebreen and Odinbreen. While the last two falls are for the most part silent, Thor's glacier was given its name because there is a continuous roar coming from inside the falls, the sound reverberating throughout the mountains. Climbing the falls can be life threatening as its crevasses are continually closing and opening, until they eventually become part of the flat Austerdalsbreen glacier.

Vårstølen – Supphellebreen

Just below Tungastølen, the narrow and wild Snauedalen valley runs into the main valley. There is a short but splendid footpath through Snauedalen where it feels as if you are walking along the bottom of a shaft between precipitous mountains, while the glacier protrudes

from the mountains above. The ice falls from the Veslebreen glacier that ends in a narrow crevice just above the valley floor is particularly beautiful. Farther out toward Fjærland, you reach the steep Supphellebreen glacier, which divides into two parts. Ice avalanches constantly tumble from the upper part over steep polished mountainsides. Down below, the glacier is 'reborn' as an enormous cone of ice blocks. You can also reach this glacier by car. Here you can sit as if in a theater and watch the ice come crashing down. The force of the fall crushing the ice, accompanied by a ferocious roar echoing and rumbling through the mountains is fascinating drama. You can stand for hours watching the glacier simply hanging there, seeming to defy the force of gravity.

Flatbrehytta and Flatbreen

From the Øygard farm in the Supphelledalen valley a good trail leads up to the self-service cabin Flatbrehytta, one of the most popular places to start or end a hike on Jostedalsbreen. Even if you do not plan to go onto the glacier itself, the view and the Flatbreen glacier's snout are worth the trip. Admittedly, the climb can be tough. It is, after all, about 1000 meters, but you are rewarded when you reach the top. It is not just that the view over Fjærlandsfjorden and toward the mountain area that stretches south and east is overwhelming, but also that the walk along the edge of the glacier can be rewarding. The Flatbreen glacier has, in fact, pushed a large terminal moraine that has formed a dam creating a little lake, Flatbrevannet. This area provides an excellent lesson as to how many of our lakes and ponds have been formed. You can walk along the ridge of the moraine and over to the edge of the Supphellebreen glacier where there is a 1000-meter drop down to the Supphelledalen valley.

A campsite at Kvitevarden on the passage between Fjærland and Lunde in Jølster. The Jølstervatn lake and Marabreen glacier in their winter setting below.
Photo: Bjørn Wold

The Flatbrehytta cabin is self-service, so you can spend the night without having to carry in your own food. Farmer and certified guide, the late Anders Øygard, who built the cabin, has gone up and down from his farm more than a thousand times, often carrying heavy loads of food, firewood, and other necessities. Think about that when you have struggled to the top or are heading back down again.

Bøyastølen – Lunde

One of the easiest crossings on the Jostedalsbreen glacier begins deep in the Bøyadalen valley. The climb is steep, but the path is easy to follow, as people and livestock have taken this route from time immemorial. Hiking on the glacier is restricted to an area of just a kilometer from the lower edge of the Marabreen glacier.

The path down to Lunde is steep with glaciers and precipices as part of the panoramic view in every direction. Ahead of you lies the narrow Kjøsnesfjorden, with its mirror-like surface, running into the Jølstravatnet lake.

Today this hike is easy to combine with a car trip. The new tunnel from Lunde to Fjærland enables you to return to where you started in about a quarter of an hour.

Oldeskaret

One of the oldest routes from Jølster to Nordfjord goes through the beautiful Oldeskaret. The trip is only six to seven kilometers long, and takes you through some of Norway's most magnificent mountain and glacial landscapes. It is a bit of a climb in the beginning, but that only makes the pleasure of having arrived, and your appreciation of the view, even better. As you climb up through the valley, you are surrounded by a dramatic landscape where photo opportunities abound.

From Jølster, the trail starts from the Høyset farm deep in the Stardalen valley and follows the Haugadalen valley all the way up to Storevatnet lake. At the north end of this lake you go through Oldeskaret, down to the Brigsdalen valley in Olden. On the way you pass the long Haugabreen glacier that today ends barely a kilometer above the trail. If you have time, it is absolutely worth a visit.

Brigsdalsbreen

The Brigsdalsbreen glacier in Olden is the most visited ice fall of all in the Jostedalsbreen glacial area. In the olden days, tourists were rowed over Oldevannet from Sunde and traveled by horse and carriage in to the glacier. When the weather is at its best, this landscape is one of the most beautiful in Norway: the large lakes lie between the gray-green mountains, and waterfalls hang like bands from shining glaciers under a deep blue sky. For many, this is the quintessence

Sleep-walking is not a good idea at Skåla. It is a long way to the bottom.
Photo: Anne Kjos-Wenjum

of western Norway's fjord landscape and cannot be found anywhere else in the world.

Today a road runs along the lake into Brigsdal, where there is a tourist center with food and lodging. It was the relatively easy approach to the ice falls that made the Brigsdalsbreen glacier a major tourist magnet.

Today you can choose whether to walk the short distance from the parking lot, or be transported by horse and carriage up to the little lake in front of the glacier.

The Brigsdalsbreen glacier is advancing rapidly, and the front of the glacier presents itself as an assemblage of blocks and chasms in a beautiful display of white and blue blended with the brown of stones and earth. It is the heavy snowfalls of the 1980's that are on their way down the glacier, and in a few years this little lake may be gone, filled with ice and rocks. Here you can see in miniature how, back when all of Norway was slowly being covered

46

by ice, the glaciers once moved forward and crushed everything in their path.

Halfway between Oldevatnet and Brigsdal, you pass the Åbrekke farms, which were largely destroyed during the so-called 'little ice age' around 1750. The tiny Brenndalsbreen glacier, today barely visible from the road, had at that time advanced significantly and fell over the hillside. The air blast in front of the avalanche totally destroyed the farms below, and much of the cultivated land was covered with blocks of ice.

Bødalsseter, in Bødalen, is one of the many green and fertile areas that borders the great glacier.
Photo: Finn Loftesnes

Skålatårnet

One of Norway's most remarkable self-service cabins, Skålatårnet, can be found on the Skåla mountain above Loen. It is an exhausting climb, almost 2000 meters up from the beautiful Lovatnet lake, but

the trail is easy and well prepared. The tower at the top is an attraction in itself. It was originally intended as a convalescence center for people suffering from tuberculosis! On the way up you pass beautiful waterfalls, and the view gets increasingly grand the higher you get. The stone-covered path, parts of it in the form of steps, has an impressive construction. It was the district medical officer, a man named Kloumann, who had the idea of building this amazing stone tower. With its thick walls – more than a meter and a half – it resembles a castle from the Middle Ages. The tower was built in 1891. Kloumann died the same year, and never had the privilege of seeing his project completed. It was his successor and his friends who constructed the steps up to the tower.

If you do not want to spend the night at the top, you should plan between ten and twelve hours for the round-trip.

Goat herding is an important activity for farmers in Erdalen.
Photo: Anne Kjos-Wenjum

Bødalsseter

At the end of the Lovatnet lake, the Bødalen valley lies to the east.

Facing page: Lodalskåpa is the highest and most distinctive peak on Jostedalsbreen.
Photo: Finn Loftesnes

The Tverrelva river in Sunn-
dalen.
Photo: Anne Kjos-Wenjum

Today you can drive along the north side of the lake. From here you can see, among other things, the Ramnefjellet mountain's enormous scarred surface, where a powerful landslide resulted in tragedy. The road ends where the Bødalen valley swings toward the south and flattens out. From here it is just under a kilometer to Bødalsseter, where DNT has a self-service cabin.

Bødalssetra lies in an idyllic setting with several houses arranged along a 'street' – unusual for western Norway. An easy trail leads in to the Bødalsbreen glacier, with its spectacular blue ice, ending in a delta leading to a small lake. Here you can observe how glaciers and water work the land. On the way in you pass a large terminal moraine. The glacier reached here during the 'little ice age', that is, around 1750. Within the terminal moraine there are many smaller moraines that illustrate how the ice has formed the landscape. Bødalsseter is, additionally, the most popular starting point for climbing Lodalskåpa.

Erdalen

The Erdalen valley, which stops at the end of the Strynevatnet lake, is, along with the Sunndalen valley a bit further north, one of the nicest valleys around the Jostedalsbreen glacier. The road into Greidung eventually becomes a cart path and ends as a trail to Velte-dalssætra, a self-service cabin, about an hour's hike from where the road stops at Greidung. On the valley floor there is an interesting outwash plain where the course of the river changes from year to year. Here you can see the stages of vegetation characteristic to Norway since the ice age. There is a good trail into the valley and up Ulvestigen where there are some unusually steep and wild ice falls on the mountain wall on the other side of the valley. When an ava-lanche occurs here, you have a front row seat and can watch with horror as the forces of nature crush the blue ice to powder on its way down the stone cliffs. On warm summer days, waterfalls hang like bridal veils.

From the top of Ulvestigen it is just a few hundred meters over to the Erdalsbreen glacier. This ends in a flat glacier tongue surround-ed by impressive smooth round rocks and barren mountain ridges, revealing that nature has been at work here for thousands of years.

The Sunndalen valley

The Sunndalen valley ends at Folven a bit above Hjelle in Oppstryn. The trip into the valley is a journey through a fantastic display of western Norway's fertile natural surroundings. The blue-green glacier stream has some of the best rapids, falls and pools. First you follow a somewhat overgrown farm trail to what was once the Sunn-dalen farm, from there you follow a good cattle trail in to Sunndals-sætra with its many seters (summer farms).

It is here the trail from Sognskardet ends, as does the trail from the Sognskardsbreen glacier. On the way in to this glacier you pass the beautiful Sognskardsvatna lakes. Many reliable pollen tests have shown that this area was once covered with forest, and that the Jostedalsbreen glacier, as we know it, was non-existent.

HOW IS A GLACIER FORMED?

What conditions must exist for a glacier to be formed? Exact figures for temperature or precipitation cannot be given, except that it has to be below zero degrees Celsius for a certain period of the year, and there must be precipitation during this period. There must be snow, but not necessarily great quantities of it. The inner parts of the Antarctic and Greenland are like deserts, with very little snowfall during the year. But it is cold all year, so that there is little melting. It is the balance between precipation as snow and the melt-off that is important. In order to form a glacier, and for the glacier to be maintained, the amount of snow that falls must exceed the amount of snow that melts every year.

If the summer is not long enough and warm enough to melt all the seasonal snow, an excess of snow accumulates. Over time it changes and the snow becomes coarser and coarser, slowly turning into ice. When this layer becomes thicker, it begins to move. It slides down the inclines and thus a glacier is born. By definition, a glacier is always in motion.

From snow to ice

New fallen snow is usually light. With temperatures well below freezing, the specific weight of this snow is about 0.1 g/cm³. This is the type of snow we associate with lovely crystalline flakes. It is difficult to find two identical snow crystals, but all are shaped like hexagons.

In the mountains, new snow seldom stays on the ground for long because the wind promptly blows it away. When the snow is swirled up by the wind, the fine crystals break apart, and the snow becomes compact. As more snow falls, the bottom layers of snow become even more densely packed.

Even in the high mountains and on the glaciers there are periods of mild weather in the winter. This leads to melting, and rain often falls for short periods

An exciting ice ridge on Svardalsbreen between Fjær-land and Veitastrond. The bands in the ice can almost be considered growth rings. Photo: Leif Strand

The Bøyabreen glacier in Fjærland has grown considerably in recent decades. Photo: Finn Loftesnes

of time. The water sinks a bit deeper into the snow before it freezes, and gradually increases the density, or specific weight, of the snow. This process is constantly taking place throughout the summer, so that snow that has survived one summer usually has a weight of 0.5-0.6 g/cm^3. Such snow is called 'firn' in professional terminology.

The further conversion from snow crystals to ice crystals happens slowly, essentially with re-crystallization, in which the large crystals grow at the expense of the small. The process is hastened by the yearly addition of melt water or rain water from the surface,

Hiking on the Nigardsbreen glacier.
Photo: Finn Loftesnes

eventually creating larger and larger layers of ice. With a density of a little over 0.8 g/cm³ there is no way for air to pass through the mass. When this happens, we have glacier ice.

Movement

The force of gravity insures glacier movements. With strong enough pressure, the ice behaves like a plastic mass, which slowly begins to slide outwards and downwards. The speed of the glacier is partially dependent on its thickness and the steepness of the terrain under it. The movement is not only a result of slippage along the rock floor, but also because of interior deformities in the ice mass. Glacier tongues that branch into narrow valleys are, as a rule, thickest in the middle. Because the thickness decreases, and friction increases, along the valley walls, the speed is consequently reduced.

On the relatively flat area at the top of the Jostedalsbreen glacier, the ice usually moves from one to ten meters in the course of a year. Down in the steep valleys the velocity increases significantly, and where it is steepest the ice moves from one to two meters a day. How much of this movement is due to slippage along the rock floor and how much is due to deformities in the ice mass varies from place to place. In Norway it is the thickness of the ice and the degree of the incline that determines this, while the temperature of the ice is also a factor in other places in the world. It is not easy to measure the slide against the rock floor, but this is actually done on some glaciers. Such measurements have shown that about a third of the speed is due to sliding while the rest is due to inner deformations in the glacier.

Camping at Ramnane.
Photo: Finn Loftesnes

The Austerdalsbreen glacier is a prime site for glacial research. It is still possible to find pieces of measuring equipment that was placed here in the 1950s. These studies contributed to a new understanding of the movement of valley glaciers. Photo: Nils Haakensen

With a mass of such size and plasticity as a glacier, you might think that it would move steadily and calmly. Detailed measurements show this is not the case. On the contrary, it moves in fits and starts. The average velocity over a 24-hour period varies little from day to day, but there are marked seasonal variations. In the winter the movement is often only a third of what it can be in the summer. This is partly because meltwater in and under the glacier has a lubricating effect during the summer.

How thick is a glacier?

Many glacier hikers have probably wondered how much ice is beneath their feet. When they peek down glacier crevasses they rarely see farther than 20 to 30 meters, but glaciers are considerably thicker.

At the end of the 1980's, surveys established the thickness of large areas of the Jostedalsbreen glacier. The results showed that the greatest depths, around 500 meters, can be found where the glacier is relatively flat over a large area. Where the glacier branches, the thickness of the ice is usually about 150 to 300 meters, while the glacer domes are generally thin, often not more than about 50 meters thick.

Japanese researchers drew a 50 m core of ice from the top of Høgste Breakulen in the spring of 1987. Here, the drill is being adjusted. Photo: Bjørn Wold

Tungastølen in Veitastrond with active summer farms, and a tourist cabin. Photo: Finn Loftesnes

Growing or melting?

If we were to go back to the previous century, we would find that all Norwegian glaciers were larger than they are today. Most of them had their greatest spread after the ice age in the middle of the 1700's. This period is popularly called 'the little ice age.' This was also true of the Jostedalsbreen glacier which had its greatest expansion in recorded history around 1750. Since then it has receded. This has not been a steady process, and most glaciers have had short periods of growth. Recession was particularly significant from about 1930 to 1970.

In the early 1960's more snow fell than melted during the summer on the Jostedalsbreen glacier's highest areas, and the glacier slowly began to expand again. This meant that some outlet glaciers lengthened quickly, while others stopped receding.

What happens when a glacier expands or recedes? To explain this, we must consider that a glacier is multi-dimensional: it has both area and volume. Glaciologists talk about a glacier's 'mass balance' when they determine whether a glacier is expanding or receding. Mass balance, as the words suggest, is a balance between

Supphellebreen in 1974. This regenerated glacier has grown substantially in recent years. Photo: Bjørn Wold

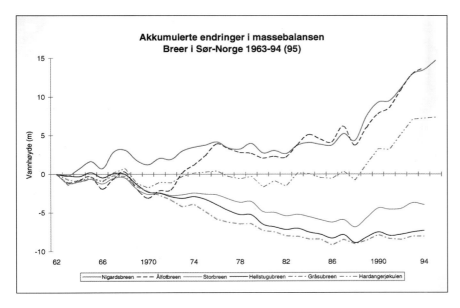

Akkumulerte endringer i massebalansen
Breer i Sør-Norge 1963-94 (95)

The Norwegian Polar Institute began measuring the mass balance on the Storbreen glacier in Jotunheimen in 1948, while the Norwegian Water Resources and Energy Administration (NVE), initiated measurements of a number of glaciers in 1962-63. The measurements show that the westernmost glaciers in southern Norway have been relatively stable or increased during the past 30 years, while the total volume of Jotunheimen's glaciers has decreased steadily up to the 1990's. In more recent years, all of the glaciers have increased. Diagram: The Norwegian Water Resources and Energy Administration (NVE).

two masses: the gain, accumulation, and the loss, ablation. The positive mass of a glacier is the amount of new snowpack or the amount that has accumulated on the glacier in the course of a year. On the negative side, we have ablation, the amount of snow and ice that melts, slides or calves over a year. When the positive effect – the addition of new snow – is greatest, the glacier expands, and when the negative effect is greatest, it recedes. Because this does not occur uniformly over the entire glacier, and the movement of the glacier also plays an important role, changes in the mass balance will not affect the glacier front for several years. When we observe that a glacier has moved forward, it can be the result of something that happened higher up on the glacier many years previously.

To calculate the amount of precipitation on the glacier, one measures the depth and the specific weight of the snow in fixed locations. Then precipitation can be converted to volume of water, a figure necessary to compare accumulation and ablation. At the end of the summer the amount of snow and ice that has melted is measured and this is also converted into volume of water. When accumulation and ablation are compared, one can determine whether the total glacier volume, or mass balance, has increased or decreased during a given year. It takes many years with the same tendencies before a fluctuation is registered as accumulation or ablation of the glacier front. If the mass balance varies a great deal from year to year, this may mean that there have been no real changes in the dimensions of the glacier.

Glacier rivers

Rivers that come from a glacier area often behave quite differently than other rivers. They also look different. While water in normal rivers appears clear or has a light blue color, glacier rivers appear greener and can become completely gray. This is because glacier water contains green algae from the melting snow, and the fact that the water transports large amounts of fine mud. This is eroded from the rock floor under the glacier as it slides downward. When the melted water reaches the bottom of the glacier it carries with it rock-flour.

As the water rises in the glacier rivers the color becomes more gray, and the roar of the river increases. This happens because the river, having become so swollen, carries larger particles from the glacier. These can be sand and gravel, but will eventually include rocks of all sizes. This is mostly material that has been eroded from the rock floor under the glacier in the course of the winter, and is now being carried away by the melted water. Large quantities of material can be carried out in this way. About 10,000 metric tons of silt and sand is transported down from Nigardsbreen each year, along with an equal amount of gravel and stone. There is a steady transport of sediments all summer, but the largest quantities come with the floods. During major floods, the quantities carried down from the Nigardsbreen glacier can be so large that it would take several big trucks removing a load a minute to get rid of the mass.

This enormous quantity is transported by glacier rivers to more level areas where it is deposited in outwash plains, as at the Fåbergstølssanduren outwash plain. It can

Glacier rivers leave large deposits of gravel and sand as they run into the lakes around the glacier. New deltas are created, seen here in Tunsbergdal's reservoir. Since this is used as a regulating reservoir for the Leirdøla power station, the delta will be dry during some of the summer months. In dry summers, this can lead to drought and the whirling glacial winds can spread large deposits of fine sand over the valley. Photo: Bjørn Wold

also be deposited in lakes and ponds at the front of the glaciers. These will gradually be filled and disappear. The Norwegian Water Resources and Energy Administration (NVE) has measurements and calculations which show that about 400,000 metric tons of material is eroded away from the rock floor by Jostedalsbreen yearly. This means the glacier, on average, erodes about 0.3 mm of rock per year.

It is not just this immense transport of rock debris that separates glacier rivers from other rivers. The water coming from a glacier is naturally much colder . These rivers also have a completely different cycle in terms of water volume. While an ordinary river swells when it rains, it is as a rule the opposite with a glacier river – rain contributes little to the melting of a glacier. However, sunlight and high temperatures mean a great deal. Glacier rivers are therefore most swollen when the weather is warm. They also have a daily rhythm; such that they are most swollen in the evening and usually easiest to cross early in the morning.

Traces from the far more extensive glaciers of old can be recognized in many areas. Here, one can clearly see how large the Fåbergstølssbreen glacier was 250 years ago. Photo: Bjørn Wold

Glaciers come and go

During the last 2.6 million years we have had four major ice ages alternating with warm intervals when the glaciers melted down completely and disappeared. However it is only the very last ice age, which began about 70,000 years ago, that we understand in detail.

We do not know much about the glaciers' changes during this period, except for the fact that about 13,000 years ago temperature changes resulted in a melt that 9000 years later left the entire

Surrounding vegetation shows how far the Nigardsbreen glacier had progressed by 1750. This entire valley is now a nature reserve; it is one of the finest examples of moraine and vegetation chronology in all of Norway. Photo: Bjørn Wold

country ice free, except for scattered glaciers in the mountains. The climate was increasingly warm, but pollen tests from the Sunndalen valley show that the Jostedalsbreen glacier began to grow again 5000 years ago, probably because the winter precipitation increased. Up until that time the climate was warmer than it is today. Extensive forests covered large parts of what is now mountain plateau, as for example on the Hardangervidda and Finnmarksvidda plateaus.

The 'little ice age'

Around 1650 the climate becomes worse, in particular the summers become colder. This causes the glacier to accumulate mass, and the glacier gradually make its way down into the valleys. The glacier tongues shoot out over terrain that has been ice free for thousands of years, pushing trees, stones and gravel in front of them. This expansion culminates around 1750, when the glaciers begin to recede. The results of this expansion can be seen everywhere in the mountains in the form of arched terminal moraines and parallel lateral moraines in front of today's glaciers. The difference in the vegetation in front of and behind the outer terminal moraines are rather striking. In front of the moraines it is lush and green, as the vegetation here is almost 9000 years old. Between the moraine and the glacier there is almost only gravel and stone – 250 years has not been enough to establish a new foundation for vegetation.

Around the Jostedalsbreen glacier the 'little ice age' had rather catastrophic consequences. We know the details very well because the farmers complained to the king and wanted to have their taxes reduced because of the damage caused by the ice. In most of the valleys much of the grazing land was lost. At Nigardsbreen, at the top of Jostedalen, the Nigard farm was totally ruined. As the local minister, Pastor Foss, described it in 1750: "In August of 1743, not only did the glacier shoot forward 100 arm lengths and even more in width, but it tore up houses, turning them upside down and pushing them in front of itself along with great amounts of earth, gravel and stones from the depths."

Damage at the Nordfjord side of the glacier was also extensive, in part because the west side is steeper so there is a greater danger of avalanches. As early as 1693, a total of 36 farms had sought tax relief because of avalanches and ice on cultivated land.

The harvest during these cold years was also poor, and Foss writes, for example, that the grain often froze. After it reaches its maximum, around 1750, the glacier begins to recede again, although there are occasional advances. About 1930, the Nigardsvatnet lake began to form in front of the glacier and today the glacier tongue is on dry land some hundred meters above the lake. This is, in fact, how quickly changes can occur.

Charting the recession of the Nigardsbreen glacier from its height in around 1748 to its low point at the end of the 1980s. In recent years, it has gradually expanded. Compare with the picture on page 63.

Rock slides and floods

You do not travel in the valleys around Jostedalsbreen in the spring without realizing that small slides and avalanches are daily fare. Every night in the spring, melting water freezes in crevasses and cracks, and ice, as we know, expands when it freezes. This creates tension on the steep mountainsides. Often it is only small stones and small amounts of earth and gravel that are shaken loose, but occasionally major catastrophes occur.

The Lovatnet lake lies on the west side of the Jostedalsbreen glacier and is surrounded by high and very steep mountains. It is here that two of recorded history's most catastrophic landslides have occurred. The first landslide was in 1905. At that time enormous masses of rock loosened from Ramnefjellet mountain on the west

In the 18th century, Hugleik Tungøien brought the farmers' complaints about the glacier's destruction in Oldedalen to the king in Copenhagen. On his homeward journey from one of these excursions, he lost his life. A memorial stone in his honor has been placed in Oldedalen. Photo: Bjørn Wold

Ramnefjell and Nesdal in Loen. Scarring from the major rock slides can still be seen on the mountain at the right. Photo: Bjørn Wold

side of the lake and created a gigantic wave that washed away farms and land around the entire lake. In all, 61 people were killed and property damages were enormous.

In 1936 an even greater landslide occurred at the same mountain, and this time 74 people were killed and again the damages were extensive. You comprehend the power of nature when you realize that when the second landslide occurred the water level in the lake rose 13 meters!

Accidents and avalanches also occur on and near glaciers. Almost every year tourists are killed or injured because they break the most elementary rules. Some die, however, as a result of unfortunate circumstances. For example, a Dutch family was killed in the Krundalen valley when about 250,000 metric tons of ice dropped 700 meters from the Baklibreen glacier, a little tributary that had not had an avalanche in man's memory. The family was killed instantaneously, and it was not until two years later when the ice had melted that the family's remains were found.

Other accidents occur when people walk too close to the ice portals where a river emerges from a glacier. Internal slides in a glacier can block the river. But this blockage can suddenly disappear, filling the portal with masses of ice and raging waters within seconds. Such an accident occurred at the Nigardsbreen glacier some years ago. Two people were killed by ice blocks carried by the water, while a handful of others narrowly escaped the same fate.

Always respect posted signs and protective railings, they are put there for a reason!

Following page: Contrasts along a glacier's ice front are often striking. Here, at the Bergsetbreen glacier, the ice and the green meadows with red campions and babies' slippers are only a few hundred meters apart. The stone in the background provides a home for the yellow-green "map lichen." In these extreme locations it has no competition from other plants. Photo: Tom Dybwad

In the winter, one must be extremely aware of the danger of avalanches. The air blast preceding the avalanche can reach a speed of 300 km per hour. Photo: Marit Orheim Mauritzen

PLANT AND ANIMAL LIFE

The immigrants arrive

When the great masses of ice slowly melted away and Norway emerged, it was not long before the first seeds came rushing in on frozen winter soil from the ice-free areas to the south and west of the glacier. Yes, the climate was harsh, but the first plants had no competitors and the soil was virginal and rich in minerals. For those that could withstand the climate, the area was a paradise. As it became warmer, stronger competitors arrived and, in order to survive, the first immigrants were continually squeezed in toward the glacier. As time went by, wave after wave of plants and animals arrived. Slowly they conquered the land, and under changing climatic conditions, found their niche, thus creating the natural surroundings we see today.

Walking through the forested valleys and up toward the edge of the glacier's stone and gravel plateau, you can see this thousand-year old battle of the elements pass in review. Even though your path will bring you from the fertile and younger to the older and tougher vegetation, we find it natural to describe those that came first, the algae, and then tell you why and how this area came to be.

Drooping saxifrage thrives on open gravel and sand and little competition. The flowers on the crown are usually sterile and purely decorative. The species virtually always propagates through the red, grainy buds on its stem. These are pure clones of the mother plant and move with wind and water to new growth areas in the vicinity. Photo: Leif Ryvarden

Algae – our first immigrants

The title sounds perhaps like a provocation because algae are something most people associate with salt water, swaying kelp, and seaweed. Algae, however, are found everywhere. One of the most amazing is the type you see as red flecks on snow drifts and glaciers all over Norway.

This ice alga (Chlamydomonas nivalis) is one-celled and swims using two swinging filaments. When the ice and snow begin to melt, the alga wakes up from its hibernation and swims in the melted water to the surface where it absorbs sunlight and begins

its photosynthesis. It is equipped with red pigments for protection against the sunlight, making the snow red. If the sunlight is too strong, it swims back down into the snow again, and that is the reason the spots on the snow can vary from day to day. The alga divides and forms colonies which can become rather large. When winter returns it encapsulates itself inside a thick shell and hibernates until spring.

These algae are an important part of the food chain for many other organisms such as small insects, roundworms, crustaceans and fungi which in turn are eaten and become food for other organisms. In this way, the algae form a kind of ground floor in the large ecosystem of glacier and naked rock.

Lichens – mountain trailblazers

You see them everywhere in the mountains, from the highest windblown peaks, to the polished stones at the glacier's front, to the driest moors in the country. Where every other organism has given up, lichens grow. They are the vanguard of all other life forms that follow. From the moment the first Norwegian rock or mountaintop emerged after the ice age, lichens were there. First as crustaceous lichens and later as shrub and leaf lichens. Where lichens grew, other plants and small animals gained a foothold.

Lichens are compound organisms consisting of a fungus and an alga where the fungus takes care of the water and the alga takes care of the photosynthesis. On the exterior layer, the fungus lie like protective bark, permitting an unbelievable tolerance to dryness and temperature changes, but this also has its price in the form of extremely slow growth. Lichens tolerate enormous variations in temperature, from plus 20 to minus 40 degrees Celsius for weeks at a time, often combined with a biting wind and a howling storm with razor sharp ice crystals and snow flakes. In the summer the same species must be able to tolerate temperatures up to 60 degrees Celsius when the summer sun can bake a dark stone all day. All other organisms would have succumbed to such great temperature variations.

One of the most common lichen in Norway is the yellow-green *Rhizocarpon geographicum,* in Norway referred to as 'map lichen'. The expression 'map lichen' comes because a borderline is formed when individuals of one type of lichen

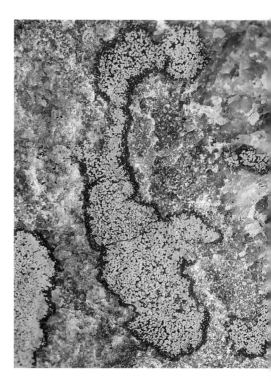

meet individuals of another type of lichen. It is usually the 'map lichen' that first occupy the polished stones and mountains when the glacier disappears from an area.

Another type of pioneer lichen is saffron lichen. It is rarely more than a few centimeters in diameter, but tolerates sudden frosts and moving soil. Saffron lichen is therefore found along almost all glaciers, patches of snow and flood areas where the water-soaked earth 'moves' with frost and thaws. The name comes from its saffron red underside.

Spring moss spreads its carpet of green in the mountains wherever there are springs, cold marshy areas or brooks. This moss has the advantage of thriving in icy water, but without this water, it is quickly surpassed by more aggressive varieties of moss. Photo: Bjørn Wold

Mosses – pioneers between lichens and flowers

Mosses grow faster than lichens, and if there are reasonable water conditions, mosses will quickly win in the competition with lichens. An important factor for mosses' life strategy and ecology is that almost all lack roots and vascular vessels, which means they cannot absorb water from the ground and carry it up to the leaves. To compensate, the leaves have strong cell walls, and this means that mosses can dry out for weeks at a time and then come to life within minutes when rain or dew arrive. All these growth characteristics explain what mosses represent.

Soot mosses can be found in nearly all areas where water is melting in the summer, particularly where the snow remains a long time. As the name suggests, they are black and also short, and most people do not recognize them as mosses, but simply see soil that is black and has a silvery glow. Such an environment has the disadvantage that the growth period is short, and it is not rare for the soot mosses to skip a season because the snow drifts simply do not melt. But there is still some light that penetrates the snow allowing for some respiration even though at a very slow pace.

Flowers arrive

After lichens and mosses had established the first colonies, it did not take long before the first seeds of flowering plants followed. The climate close to the glacier is harsh, with long winters and cold summers. Since the soil thaws, freezes and moves, roots are subjected to heavy stress. Further, there are not many insects near the glacier, so that pollination by insects does not often occur. On the other hand, all mountain plants near a glacier are perennials, so that they can, over a period of years, slowly build up reserves and be prepared if a good summer comes along. What then are the advantages of growing here at the edge of the glacier? Well, there is enough light and water and, as mentioned previously, the competition is minimal. Because of this, there is often an abundance of species which can survive here on the edge.

Because there are few insects and pollination is random, many species have evolved to be viviparous, meaning that the mother plant develops living seed plants. These sprout on the mother plant and develop small roots and leaves. This is important to the local environment, but this type of dispersal over long distances is not tolerated by the seed plants. They will die. Alpine hairgrass is, for example, a typical glacier plant that propagates in this manner.

Alpine hairgrass is a typical pioneer, growing along the mountains' glacial rivers and gravel flats. This plant has adapted to the hard climate by taking a shortcut and developing small seed plants directly on the mother plant. These fall off in the fall, and are very vulnerable.
Photo: Leif Ryvarden

Other typical pioneer species common around the Jostedalsbreen glacier are mountain sorrel, starwort mouse ear, alpine pearlwort, alpine poa, dwarf cudweed, alpine speedwell and dwarf willow.

Not only is the ice front constantly changing, but the large glacier rivers undergo major flooding for long periods of time in the summer when much of the winter snow is carried down to the fjord. How vegetation developed along these rivers with their special environment can best be seen at Fåbergstølsgrandane and in the Erdalen valley. Here it is not so much the climate but rather the unstable environment that sets the limit. The rivers wind back and forth and deposit large flats of gravel and sand which can dry up and lie there for hundreds of years before the whims of nature bring the river back again.

Mosses can conquer such river flats in a short period of time, and soon mountain oat and babies' slippers, and of course, some stray individuals from the glacier area's pioneer troops arrive. Seeds are continually washed down with flood waters. After a period of years, salt lichen establishes itself on the sand flats, and willow bushes begin to take over. If they are left alone, they will have grown to a height of two meters in 20 years time.

If left undisturbed for another 70 to 80 years a forest will cover the area.

Mountain sorrel is highly adaptable and establishes itself rather quickly on the open ground bordering our glaciers. Its winged seeds facilitate spreading by the wind. Reindeer are particularly fond of this tasty plant. Photo: Leif Ryvarden

Animal life

On a first visit to a glacier area, animal life is inconspicuous. The reason, of course, is that as plant production is modest, there is a shortage of food for the consumers, in this case the animals.

On the other hand, there will be small animals that make up the consumer chain – even small ponds and brooks on the glacier itself teem with minuscule animals. In melt water, brooks and rivers there are large numbers of insect larvae that live on algae and fungi, especially on the small, slippery, brown algae that dominate the river bottom. Eventually the animals are moved with the current down

the watercourse and many are eaten along the way by other small animals, insects and fish. In particular there are many mosquito larvae that live in this way.

Along the edges of the glacier it is almost only the snow sparrow that nests permanently. During the summer it survives almost exclusively on insects. On rocky soil, a little further away from the glacier, the stonechat has found a place to settle. Nevertheless, it is when we approach forest areas that we first encounter other types of birds. The dense hoary alder forests, so common along many of the rivers of the Jostedalsbreen glacier, can have up to 1000 mating pairs per square kilometer. This is a very high figure that testifies to the excellent conditions for both plants and animals.

Ermine and red fox are common around the entire glacier and can often be seen right up to the glacier's edge, particularly in years with large rodent populations. During years with an abundance of lemmings, in late summer one can see many of them lying dead on the ice. During these years one needs to be careful about the drinking water.

In recent years, deer have been more and more common in the valleys around the Jostedalsbreen glacier. During the summer the animals move all the way up to the tree line, but you have to be an early bird to catch a glimpse of a deer grazing on an open field.

THE GLACIER AS
A PASSAGEWAY

From time immemorial, people have used the glacier as a shortcut when they wanted to travel from the valley regions on the east side to the fjords on the west side, or vice versa. According to legend, the entire population of the Jostedalen valley died at the hands of the Black Death. Dialect studies clearly indicate that the valley was inhabited anew by people who crossed the glacier from Nordfjord.

However, we have no written record of these early glacier wanderers. It is not until about 1600 that we learn the names of people who

The Erdalsbreen glacier has receded substantially in the past 30 years; it would require climatic changes before it could resume its original size. Photo: Tom Dybwad

In the old days, Erdalen in Oppstryn was the last settlement cattle drives passed through before continuing across to Jostedalen.
Photo: Tom Dybwad

crossed the glacier and when and where they did so. Historic sources from this time point to close communication between Jostedalen and upper Stryn.

Before Jostedalen had a church, around 1660, the residents crossed the glacier to attend services in Oppstryn. This was not just for regular services, but for funerals and weddings as well, where the entire bridal party crossed the glacier. Almost all took the shortest route from Fåberg, at the top of the valley, through Fåbergstølsgrandane and over the glacier to Erdal in Stryn. Traffic began as early as April/May when the snow was firm and covered the crevasses. At the end of July and beginning of August, the melting of the snow on the lower parts of the glacier put an end to the traffic. Walking in this area then became extremely dangerous or even impossible because of all the exposed crevasses.

Drovers

Perhaps the most remarkable type of traffic over the glacier in earlier times was large herds of cattle. We do not know when this began, but when Pastor Foss in 1750 wrote his report to the bishop on conditions in the parish, he mentioned the cattle drives as a common occurrence. The drovers purchased calves in the northwestern part of the country, drove them over the glacier and onward to the cities and marketplaces of eastern Norway. On the way they took advantage of mountain grazing areas in Valdres and Hallingdal before the animals were sold in September.

The drovers would arrive in the Nordfjord district around Christmas time and make deals about the purchase of animals. At this time the female animals were pregnant and the farmers could estimate how many livestock they would have by summer.

In May and June the drovers returned, collected the livestock and

The self-service tourist cabin, Vetledalssetra, deep in the valley of Erdalen at Oppstryn, is owned and run by Tor Greidun, one of the few remaining certified guides. His father, Rasmus, was also a certified guide, and the family's strong ties to the glacier are illustrated by the fact that Tor's mother came from Jostedalen, on the opposite side of the glacier. Photo: Anne Kjos-Wenjum

Not all of our glaciers are expanding. Like many other glaciers farthest north in the national park, the Erdalsbreen glacier in Oppstryn has been receding over many years. The lake in front of the Erdalsbreen glacier has grown in the past 15 years, and this makes it difficult for the glacier to recapture its previous ground.
Photo: Anne Kjos-Wenjum

began the drive eastward. In particular, the route through Oppstryn and the Erdalen valley was frequently used for this traffic. If the weather was clear, the snow would freeze during the course of an evening, making the surface firm and easy for the animals to walk on. The heaviest horses were often outfitted with snowshoes. If the crust was firm enough, this went smoothly. But if the weather was mild, the animals would sink into the snow, and the journey could be strenuous, leaving the animals with bloody legs and hooves. The animals were not fed during the crossing. If the climb up the Erdalsbreen glacier was difficult, the climb down the Lodalsbreen glacier could be just as hard. Occasionally they had to bind the cows' front and hind legs together and literally slide them down the steepest hills.

We have only random figures regarding this traffic, but the biggest drive is supposed to have taken place June 28, 1886. Four drovers crossed the glacier with six horses and 168 head of cattle. The biggest sheep drive involved more than 350 head. The last cattle drive over the Jostedalsbreen glacier was in 1923.

The original mountain guides

We know that the drovers often received help from local men who, after innumerable trips in both good and bad weather, knew the glaciers like the backs of their hands. In the last century, when the first foreign tourists discovered western Norway's mountains and fjords, these men would also serve as local guides for those who wanted to see the glacier up close. For some of them, this was an extra job during the summer and they were often recommended by The Norwegian Mountain Touring Association(DNT). To better control this

Glacier guide Mikkel Mundal with a tourist. Photo: Borowed from the Mundal Hotel

Mikkel Mundal and Henry Caudler in 1903. Photo: Borrowed from the Mundal Hotel

activity, DNT began issuing an authorization for these mountain guides, and this was the origin of certified guide services.

For a fixed fee set by DNT, they would guide tourists over the glacier, and for an extra sum they also carried luggage. They had their own log book where they recorded all the details of the excursions. They were on call and had to be ready on two hours notice all summer. There were many skilled guides when DNT began granting authorizations, and in the first year, 1888, a total of 18 men were certified as guides on the Jostedalsbreen glacier. Later DNT began arranging its own courses.

The hiking gear used at that time was somewhat heavy and not always of the best quality, making a trip on the glacier with someone who did not know their limitations quite strenuous for everybody involved. A typical crossing took between 10 and 14 hours.

Occasionally, dramatic episodes occurred. One of the best known occurred when a guide crossed the glacier from Fjærland to Jølster. He had a horse with him, and at the glacier's highest point he was caught by surprise by a sudden snow storm. He realized his life was at stake and that good advice was going to be hard to come by up there. In the end, he killed the horse and crept into its belly, thus managing to save his own life. To this day, the glacier is called 'Marabreen' (the 'mare' glacier).

On another occasion, a Russian wanted to cross the glacier, but initially the guides refused because they thought he was not in good enough shape. But when the Russian offered to double his payment, nobody could resist the temptation. They set out from Fjærland to cross to Lunde in Jølster with renewed enthusiasm.

The Russian's physical condition proved to be so poor that by the time darkness fell, they had only just come down from the glacier. There was no way they could manage a 1300-meter steep descent through intricate terrain at night. To prevent the Russian from freezing to death, the guides found an overhang under which they lay down on either side of the Russian in order to keep him somewhat warm. When they arrived at their destination the next day, they collected their double fee and headed straight home again. "He was a reliable man when it came to paying up, but a sluggard at hiking," was their short comment after the trip.

Mikkel Mundal, portrait from 1901.
Photo: Borrowed from the Mundal Hotel

Anders Lunde from Jølster was a large, strong man who had crossed the glacier more than 800 times before he decided to call it a day. One of the trips he remembered best was the time he carried a sick Englishman down from the glacier: "He wasn't so heavy, but it was a bit bothersome with his big feet dragging along on the ground."

Pioneer days

We have the first thorough description of the Jostedalsbreen glacier from Pastor Foss, the local minister in Jostedalen. In 1750 he and the other pastors in the diocese were ordered by Bishop Pontoppidan in Bergen to give a description of their parishes. Foss had most likely never been up on the glacier itself, but based his report on his own ob-

Glacier guide Mikkel Mundal (second from the right), with his fellow hikers. Photo borrowed from the Mundal Hotel

servations and descriptions from his parishioners, who had more mountain and glacier experience. "This glacier is, to truly describe it, an awesome iceberg hovering above the high mountains, and it has branched down to the west in the Krondalen as well as in the Milvirsdalen valleys..." Thus begins his description. He provides detailed descriptions of crevasses, colors, cold winds that sweep down from the glacier and the thunderous sounds accompanying an avalanche.

One of the skiing heroes of the Jostedalsbreen glacier is Ole Bøyasva who, in 1788, probably completed one of history's hardest ski trips on the glacier. Starting in the morning in Fjærland, he climbed 2000 meters and skied 80 kilometers across the glacier and down to Greidung in Oppstryn, and then he made the return trip the next day! As far as we know, no one else has been inspired to follow in his footsteps.

Perhaps the real pioneer of the glacier was the Dane, G. Bohr. He was actually a music teacher and a so-called 'astronomy observer,' and in 1820 he and a Lieutenant Daa and two guides hiked past

Fåberg and climbed all the way up Lodalskåpa. This was a bold and dangerous trip considering the poor equipment they used, and Bohr describes the climb as: "...a slippery foothold between oneself and death. The first wrong step can be your last step." Afterward it was discovered they had not been on Lodalskåpa, but on a little peak leading up to it.

A few weeks later, Jotunheimen pioneers, Christian Boeck and B. M. Keilhau, arrived at Jostedalen to climb Lodalskåpa. They tried but did not succeed. The glacier made a frightening impression on them: "Enormous snow masses as far as the eye can see and innumerable glaciers make this the most terrifying area." They never returned to Jostedalen.

The man who really opened up the Jostedalsbreen glacier for Norwegians was the English mountaineer, William C. Slingsby. He first came to Jostedalen in 1874, and returned many times.

He was a daring man who, among other things, climbed down the

*This spot, at the narrowest section of the glacier between Langedalen in Veitastrond and Stardalen in Jølster, is called Bing's Hollow. Extreme wind conditions are primarily responsible for carving out this natural phenomenon. Each summer, Bing's Hollow is sustained and enlarged by melt water that collects in its base.
Photo: Bjørn Wold*

Kjenndalsbreen glacier. No one has ever attempted to do this after him – nor should they. Afterwards, Slingsby laconically described the trip as, "The most awful glacierwork I have ever done!"

At about the same time, Kristian Bing, a lawyer from Bergen, was on the glacier, and he was much more systematic than Slingsby. He visited all the glacier falls, climbed most of them, and was also the first to hike the glacier lengthwise and spend the night on the glacier. He and two local guides hiked together, and it took a total of 47 hours. That the equipment left something to be desired is evident from what one of them wrote in his journal " ...our bedroom was not exactly warm. Our shoes were frozen stiff and the blanket beneath us was frozen fast to the mountain." It was on this trip that they discovered the famous cave that has come to be called 'Bing's Hollow.'

Tourists arrive

William C. Slingsby was just one of many Englishmen who had the financial means to make trips abroad just for their own pleasure.

Slingsby at Turtagrø.
Photo: Borowed from the
Mundal Hotel

Western Norway, with its wild natural surroundings, magnificent waterfalls and large glaciers, was a natural destination for the English upper-class, for whom this was only a short trip across the North Sea.

The classic travel route for this group was to arrive at Stavanger and travel through Ryfylke and Hardanger to Sogn, where the Balholm and Mundal hotels beside Fjærlandsfjorden were a natural place to spend the night. Others traveled to the Alexandra Hotel in Loen on the west side of the Jostedalsbreen glacier. Boats and carriages transported the tourists to the entrance to the glacier, where the precipitous ice falls of the Brigsdalsbreen and Bøyabreen glaciers were two of the highlights.

A painter in front of the Supphellebreen glacier. Photo: Borowed from the Mundal Hotel

The Nigardsbreen glacier in the 1850s. This glacier has receded greatly since it reached its maximum size 100 years ago, but it is still imposing. From the book Norway and its Glaciers, *by James D. Forbes (1853).*

Facing page: A guided tour on the Nigardsbreen glacier. Photo: Bjørn Wold

In this century, cruise ships began bringing tourists into the western fjords on a small scale. Fjærland and Sogn were among the major attractions because from there it was a day trip in to the glaciers. This type of excursion is still very popular, and some fifty cruise ships visit Sognefjorden and Nordfjord each year.

From eastern Norway tourists began crossing over the Strynefjellet mountain range by horse and carriage when the Strynefjell road was opened in 1894.

Today, people traveling by car are the most important group of tourists, and can take advantage of the various types of accommodations, from the simplest campgrounds to big luxury hotels with all the amenities. The area offers numerous outdoor activities, from simple trips along marked trails to boat and helicopter excursions, salmon fishing and summer skiing. But when all is said and done, it is the fjords, mountains and glaciers that draw people back year after year to this fascinating and beautiful part of our country.

THE NATIONAL PARK AND GLACIER MUSEUMS

The Jostedalsbreen National Park

It is a long way down to the bottom. The view over the Lovatn lake.
Photo : Bjørn Wold

The idea of establishing a national park in connection with the Jostedalsbreen glacier has been around for a long time. But various conditions, in particular comprehensive plans for developing the hydropower resources in the area, resulted in the park not being

The cafe beneath the Bøya-breen glacier in Fjærland has been restored and enlarged. In consideration of the extreme weather conditions, the building is shaped like a terminal moraine and protected against possible air blasts and rock slides.
Photo: Bjørn Wold

established until 1991. At 1200 square kilometers, it is our largest national park, second only to Hardangervidda. Because of its unique geological phenomena, in addition to the national park itself, the area and valley in front of the Nigardsbreen glacier are protected by law as a natural reserve.

The purpose of establishing this national park is primarily to protect the great natural resource, which is the glacier itself, the largest on the European mainland. The intention is not only to preserve the glacier for outdoor activities, but also to protect the many cultural and natural resources around the glacier. There are few places in this country with such variety in the natural surroundings, from the fertile valleys in western Norway to the wild mountains and glaciers, while in the north and east one can find some of the most arid areas in the country. Because of this diversity there is rich vegetation in the national park area.

The work of the ice, such as grinding and carving by glacier arms, has shaped the landscape over thousands of years. The rivers carry material down to the fjord, while the water carves and changes the course of the rivers. Moraines are formed and torn down, lakes appear and disappear, all because the glacier can be compared to a living organism. Here we can experience first hand how our country was shaped.

Because of this, it was important not just to preserve the ice and the glacier itself, but also to protect part of the cultural landscape in the valleys around the glacier. Some wanted more conservation, some wanted less, but the result is something we can live with and manage for future generations. We must respect the rules that apply to protected area and try not to leave any traces of your visit behind. Never forget that we are protecting our children's heritage.

There are many places where you can obtain information about the Jostedalsbreen glacier. In addition to studying tourist brochures providing short summaries about the glacier, we strongly recommend that you visit all, or at least some, of the museums and information centers established around the Jostedalsbreen glacier.

The Norwegian Glacier Museum

As the name implies, this is a glacier museum that provides first hand information about how glaciers are born, how they have shaped our landscape and how they are used in research on climate. The museum provides an instructive introduction to the glacier's characteristics and the laws that govern its life and development. This is shown through posters and displays, models and an extensive collection of photographs. Every day fresh ice is brought in from the glacier to illustrate some of the processes occurring on the glacier itself.

The museum also has extensive documentation on the pioneers and their activities, from the old drovers to modern day skiers. Hiking and safety are given high priority.

Like a moraine, the Norwegian Glacier Museum in Fjærland traverses the base of the valley close to the fjord. The architect was inspired by glacial crevasses in his design for this museum which has had a record number of visitors each year since it opened.
Photo: Ole Martin Korsen

There is also a large theater where an intriguing film allows you to experience parts of the glacier most tourists would never see.

Jostedalsbreen National Park Centre

The park center is at the Strynsvatn lake in Oppstryn, and provides information on all aspects of the national park. The center was established on the initiative of the Ministry of the Environment and has extensive exhibits on the glacier. In addition, subjects such as geology, botany and biology in the vicinity of the glacier are focused upon through exhibits using models, text and photographs. Outside the center there is a small botanical garden with about 150 species from the national park.

The national park center has also established nature trails and culture trails in the Glomsdalen, Fosdalen, Erdalen, and Sunndalen valleys and in Flostranda in Oppstryn. There are also trails in the Brigsdalen, Bødalen and Kjenndalen valleys.

The center also illustrates how the pioneers ventured on their

The design of the Jostedals-breen National Park Centre in Oppstryn is based on the long houses used by the Vikings.
Photo: Anne Kjos-Wenjum

The Breheim Centre in Jostedalen is just outside the Nigardsbreen glacier nature reserve. This architect has also been inspired by glacial towers and crevasses. Photo: Bjørn Wold

trips of discovery, and how the local people used the glacier as a passageway. The national park center also has a theater where films about the glacier and outdoor activities on and around the glacier are shown. There are also films about vegetation and animal life. All year round, excursions, lectures, and seminars about the glacier and its natural surroundings are arranged at the center.

The Breheim Centre

This center is situated in a lovely spot close to Nigardsgrandane, at the top of the Jostedalen valley and has a view of the Nigardsbreen glacier. The center's goal is to inform the public about the natural and cultural history of the Jostedalen and Breheimen. It has a number of exciting exhibits as well as a theater with a show with slides and sound from the glacier and its surroundings.

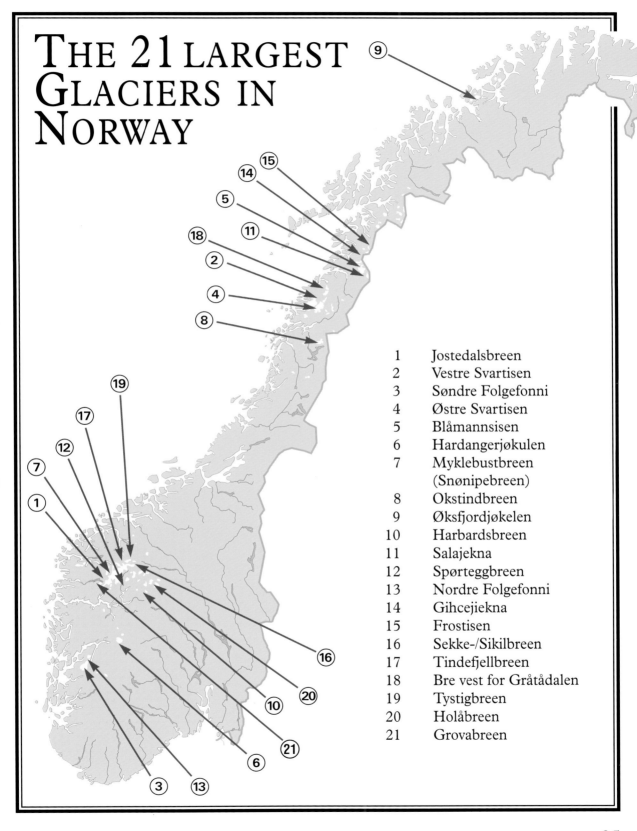

THE 21 LARGEST GLACIERS IN NORWAY

1 Jostedalsbreen
2 Vestre Svartisen
3 Søndre Folgefonni
4 Østre Svartisen
5 Blåmannsisen
6 Hardangerjøkulen
7 Myklebustbreen
  (Snønipebreen)
8 Okstindbreen
9 Øksfjordjøkelen
10 Harbardsbreen
11 Salajekna
12 Spørteggbreen
13 Nordre Folgefonni
14 Gihcejiekna
15 Frostisen
16 Sekke-/Sikilbreen
17 Tindefjellbreen
18 Bre vest for Gråtådalen
19 Tystigbreen
20 Holåbreen
21 Grovabreen

JOSTEDALSBREEN
NORWAY'S LARGEST GLACIER

© Boksenteret A/S 1996
Desktop published by Boksenteret A/S
Graphic design: Øyvind Skagmo, Boksenteret A/S
Reproductions and printing: Tangen Grafiske Senter A/S, 1996
Paper: 150 g. Galerie Art Silk

COVER PICTURES:
Front, large picture:
The Brigdalsbreen glacier with foliage in the foreground.
Photo: Jørn Areklett Omre - NN/Samfoto
Front, small picture, top:
Tourists beneath the Brigdalsbreen glacier. Mittet photo
Front, small picture, bottom:
Brigdalsbreen. Photo: Anne Kjos-Wenjum
Back, bottom:
Tourists secured by a rope, the Jostedalsbreen glacier.
Photo: Pål Hermansen - NN/Samfoto
Back, top:
View toward Glomsdalen. Photo: Anne Kjos-Wenjum

Picture on page 2:
Playing a tune on Supphellenipa.
Photo: Finn Loftesnes

ISBN: 82-7683-090-0

*Published in cooperation with the Norwegian Glacier Museum and
the Jostedalsbreen National Park Centre*

Inquiries can be sent to:

Boksenteret A/S
Postboks 3125 Elisenberg
0207 Oslo
Phone: 22 54 07 00